# Molly Mouse
## HAS A
# Party

**by Anne Giulieri**
illustrated by Natalia Moore

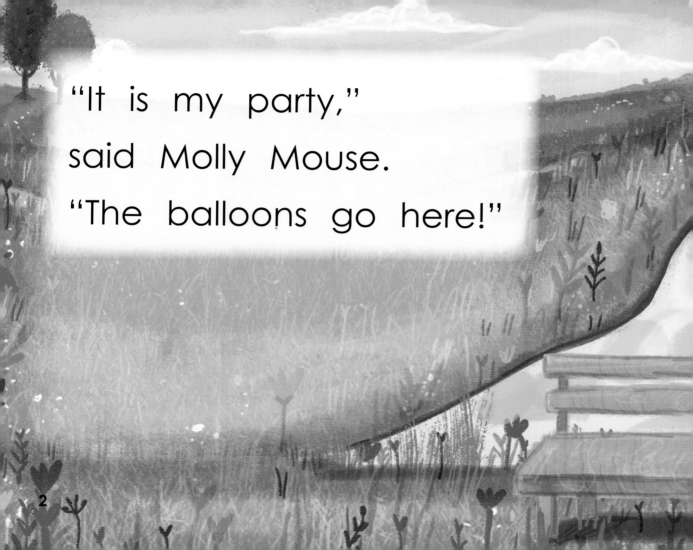

"It is my party,"
said Molly Mouse.
"The balloons go here!"

2

Tap! Tap!
"Can I come in?"
said the rabbit.

4

"You can come
to my party,"
said Molly Mouse.

Tap! Tap!

"Can I come in too?"
said the bird.

6

"You can come
to my party,"
said Molly Mouse.

7

**BANG! BANG!**

"Can I come in?"
said the fox.
"I am hungry!"

"**No!**" said Molly Mouse.
"Go away!"

9

"**Yum!**" said the fox.

The rabbit looked.
The bird looked too.

"Can the fox come in?"
said the rabbit.
"I am hungry."

"I am hungry too,"
said the bird.

13

"I am not going
to eat **you**!" said the fox.
"I am going to
eat the cake."

15

"And you can eat it, too!"
said the fox.